Research & survey in nature conservation
Conservation management of the Uplands

No. 27

Methods for monitoring heather cover

Angus MacDonald & Helen Armstrong*
Hill Vegetation Management Project
Chief Scientist Directorate (Uplands Section)
Scottish Headquarters
Nature Conservancy Council

*Present address:
Macaulay Land Use Research Institute
Pentlandfield
Roslin
Midlothian

Further copies can be obtained from
Publicity Services Branch, Nature Conservancy Council,
Northminster House, Peterborough PE1 1UA

 ISBN 0 86139 602 2

CONTENTS

	Page
Introduction	5
Monitoring Method 1: photographic monitoring of changes in heather cover	9
Objectives	9
Procedure	9
Comments on the procedure	10
Time requirements	11
Advantages and disadvantages	12
When to use this method	12
Monitoring Method 2: rapid assessment of heather utilisation on selected areas with highest risk of overgrazing	14
Objectives	14
Procedure	14
Comments on the procedure	16
Time requirements	17
Advantages and disadvantages	17
When to use this method	17
Monitoring Method 3: rapid assessment and mapping of heather utilisation over a whole site	18
Objectives	18
Procedure	18
Comments on the procedure	20
Time requirements	21
Advantages and disadvantages	21
When to use this method	21
Monitoring Method 4: estimation of heather utilisation with a precision of ± 10% in strata of low, medium and high grazing intensity	22
Objectives	22
Procedure	22
Comments on Procedure	25
Time requirements	26
Advantages and disadvantages	27
When to use this method	27
Acknowledgements	27
Appendix	28
References	29

Introduction

Heather Calluna vulgaris has been declining in many parts of Britain, particularly in England and Wales. The Nature Conservancy Council/Countryside Commission's National Countryside Monitoring Scheme (NCMS) has estimated a loss of 286 km^2 of heather-dominated vegetation in Cumbria between the 1940s and 1970s from analysis of a large sample of aerial photographs (NCC 1987). Of this loss 209 km^2 was of drier moorland dwarf-shrub heath (predominantly heather), representing a 70% loss of this vegetation type. In the Peak District, Anderson & Yalden (1981) used vegetation maps to estimate losses of 36% of heather moorland between 1913 and 1981. Much of this loss has been as a result of increased grazing pressures or as a result of direct conversion to improved pasture. Even in Scotland the NCMS has revealed surprisingly large losses of heather moorland between the 1940s and 1970s. In Grampian Region the loss of drier heather moorland was just over 25%, in Galloway there was a loss of about 63%, and in Borders Region the loss was just over 20% (NCC/CCS 1988; Sydes 1988). Heather has also disappeared as a result of similarly large losses of blanket bog. In Scotland afforestation has accounted for about half of these losses but conversion to grassland as a result of heavy grazing has been the next most important cause of loss, accounting for about a quarter of total losses.

This scale of heather loss is of concern for nature conservation in upland Britain.

Internationally, Britain is unique in still having large expanses of heather-dominated vegetation. Heathland plants, such as bell heather Erica cinerea, western gorse Ulex gallii and bristle bent Agrostis curtisii, which are abundant in parts of Britain, mostly in heather-dominated dwarf-shrub communities, have highly restricted European distributions. Britain also supports substantial proportions of the European populations of certain birds characteristic of heather moorland, including red grouse, hen harrier and merlin (Ratcliffe & Thompson 1988).

In the British context more nationally uncommon plants are associated with heather-dominated communities than with the types of grassland or conifer plantation to which heather communities have been converted. These include bog-rosemary Andromeda polifolia, alpine bearberry Arctostaphylos alpinus, dwarf birch Betula nana, Dorset heath Erica ciliaris, marsh clubmoss Lycopodiella inundata, interrupted clubmoss Lycopodium annotinum, red broomrape Orobanche alba, intermediate wintergreen Pyrola media, and small cranberry Vaccinium microcarpum. Also, certain types of western heather-dominated communities support populations of rare mosses and liverworts (Hobbs 1988). A number of the more characteristic British moorland birds are associated, to varying degrees, with heather-dominated communities and require extensive areas of heather if viable populations are to be maintained. These include red grouse, black grouse, merlin, hen harrier, short-eared owl and twite. These decline if heather is extensively replaced by grassland or afforestation (Bibby 1988; Thompson et al. 1988). The national populations of many of these are thought to be declining and they have become scarce in south-west England and much of Wales. This is particularly serious for hen harrier and merlin: British populations are only 500-600 pairs for each species.

Further loss of heather will compromise this international and national conservation interest.

One of the elements in any system designed to prevent or reverse heather loss is a set of monitoring methods which will reveal changes in heather cover on sites soon after they have happened or before they are about to happen. Four methods are described in the following pages. The first provides information about changes in heather cover after they have occurred; the remaining three methods provide information, of increasing precision, about the utilisation of heather by herbivores and the probability of future heather loss. A useful addition to these methods is a preliminary analysis of aerial photographs, if these are available. This will provide valuable information about changes in the extent of heather-dominated vegetation in the recent past (if heather cover falls below 25% it will appear to have vanished on aerial photographs). Coupled with information about management over the same period, this will help in deciding if monitoring is required.

KEY FEATURES OF HEATHER MONITORING METHODS

METHOD	OBJECTIVES	DATA COLLECTED	ANALYSIS	TIME REQUIRED PER ASSESSMENT FOR A SITE OF ABOUT 500HA (MAN-DAYS)	REPEAT PERIOD (YEARS)
1. Photographic monitoring of changes in heather cover.	(a) Permanent objective visual record of gross changes in cover. (b) Record of unexpected changes.	Photographs covering whole site from fixed points.	Semi-objective assessment of heather cover changes by comparison of photographs.	5-8 initially, 2-4 subsequently.	2-5
2. Rapid assessment of heather utilisation on selected areas with highest risk of overgrazing.	(a) Quick, approximate, assessment of proportion of most vulnerable stands subject to damaging utilisation. (b) Preliminary assessment of possible overgrazing on non-vulnerable stands.	(a) Map of distribution and extent of most vulnerable stands. (b) % shoot numbers grazed in each vulnerable stand. (c) Observations of extent of different heather growth forms. (d) Observations of grazing intensity on other vegetation types.	Approximate assessment of extent and degree of damaging utilisation on a site	2-3	1 if overgrazing of vulnerable stands, 5 otherwise.
3. Rapid assessment and mapping of heather utilisation over a whole site.	Systematic extension of method 2 to assess all heather stands on a site.	(a) Map of heather stands. (b)% shoot numbers grazed in each stand.	Comprehensive and objective assessment of extent of possible damaging utilisations.	5	For one site per local climatic region, 1 if overgrazing of non-vulnerable stands, 0 otherwise.
4. Estimation of heather utilisation with a precision of $\pm10\%$ in low, medium and high grazing intensity strata.	(a) Objective, and statistically analysable estimates of utilisation of total heather long-shoot length in strata defined using method 3. (b) Check on method 3.	Estimates of mean utilisation for each of 3 strata based on measurements of randomly sampled shoots in randomly located 20m x 20m plots.	Objective estimates of mean utilisation, with 95% confidence limits of $\pm10\%$, for areas of low, medium and high utilisation plus the extent of these categories on the site.	4-6 plus time for method 3.	Ideally, once if method 3 carried out, again after any management change.

DECISION DIAGRAM FOR USE OF DIFFERENT MONITORING METHODS

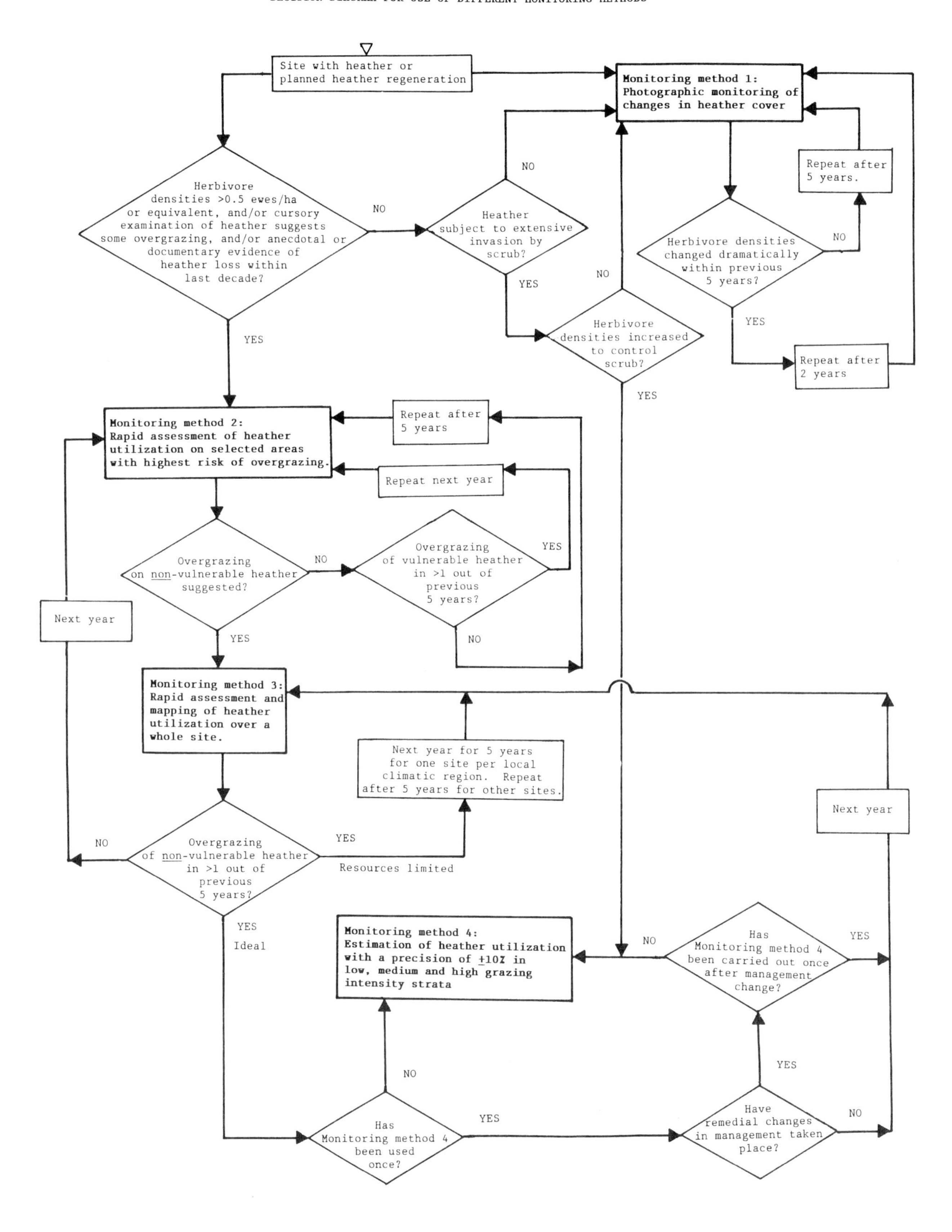

Monitoring Method 1: photographic monitoring of changes in heather cover

Objectives

The objective of this method is to provide a permanent visual record of gross changes in heather cover with respect to other types of vegetation cover, capable of recording unexpected changes.

Procedure

1 Ideally, monitoring should be carried out in June to July. Each repeat monitoring should be carried out at the same time of year.

2 Select a number of vantage points so that the whole of the site being monitored will be covered by photographs from these vantage points using a 35 mm camera fitted with a 35 mm wide-angle lens. The locations should be marked on a 1:25,000 scale map or larger scale map if available.

3 Mark each vantage point position permanently. On a large upland site some moderately conspicuous indicator, such as a fence stob, will be needed if a fixed point is to be found quickly and accurately. This should not be positioned too conspicuously but should be easily locatable by those who know its approximate position or from compass bearings to local landmarks. Each stob should be numbered - car touch-up paint tubes with an integral brush are convenient, or stobs can be more permanently numbered using a router or a pyrography iron before they are set out on site. The distance and compass bearing from the stob to the fixed point should be accurately recorded. The fixed point should be marked with a preservative-treated wooden peg, about 5 cm x 5 cm x 60 cm, driven half-way into the ground. On blanket bog with *Sphagnum*, untreated pegs and fence stobs should be used. A useful addition would be to drive in a length of iron or aluminium strip beside each peg. This would allow location of the fixed point by metal detector, should the peg go missing or become overgrown by heather or other vegetation. Alternatively, a 40 - 60 cm length of scaffolding tube could be used, driven half into the ground and with the top end closed with a wooden plug. All markers should be checked every year.

   On very rocky sites it may not be possible or necessary to use markers which have to be driven into the ground. Monitoring points can then be relocated by a combination of compass bearings to prominent landmarks and by the use of a photograph of the camera tripod *in situ* taken so as to show nearby, distinctive topographic features (distinctive lichen patterns on nearby rocks can also be useful).

4 Ideally, a good quality solid tripod should be used, levelled so that the centre column is perpendicularly above the marked fixed point. The tripod head should be adjustable and be graduated in the vertical axis. On successive occasions photographs should be taken at the same height above ground level, along the same compass bearing, at the same inclination, and using the same type of camera, lens and film.

5 A good quality camera should be used - 35 mm format is adequate - with a good quality 35 mm lens. A motor winder can speed up picture taking

and a data back, which will imprint a number code, date or time (usually in the lower right corner of the frame), will aid identification of photographs at the analysis stage. These are optional. Each photograph should be taken using a cable release to minimise vibration.

6 Two camera bodies should be used. One should be loaded with a medium speed monochrome film such as Ilford FP4 or Kodak Plus-X, the other with a good quality medium speed colour slide film (64-200 ASA) such as Kodachrome 64.

7 Photographs should be taken at a standard aperture of f8. If any foreground appears within the photograph frame the lens should be focused at about 20 - 30 m. With a wide angle lens this will give sharp results in the foreground as well as in the distance.

8 Photographs should be taken in bright but overcast, haze-free, more-or-less windless conditions, or as near to this ideal as is practicable.

9 At each fixed vantage point each photographic shot should be taken twice in both monochrome and colour.

10 If the area being monitored is being photographed at a shallow angle and there is a distinct heather boundary, a scaling aid (e.g. a ranging pole) should be positioned on the boundary within the picture frame.

11 A careful record should be made of what each photograph represents as it is being taken.

12 Film should be processed as soon after being exposed as possible. Ideally, archival processing should be used.

13 Photographs should be inspected and compared with previous photographs soon after they have been taken. Changes in the pattern of heather cover should be analysed and boundaries of heather-dominated areas transferred to a topographic base map. Any difficult points of interpretation should be checked in the field. Use the changes in heather area on the base maps from successive monitoring to assess the proportionate gains and losses in heather area.

14 The two sets of negatives, prints and slides should be stored in two separate places in cool, dry, dark conditions.

15 Repeat every two years where stocking densities are high, or have dramatically changed either up or down within the previous five years. Otherwise repeat every five years.

Comments on the procedure

Step 1 Time of year for photographic monitoring is not critical although each monitoring occasion should take place at the same time of year. The contrast between different vegetation types (except for bracken) is greatest during October to April but good light conditions are more likely during the remainder of the year. If other monitoring or grazing assessment methods are also being used then it would make sense to undertake photographic monitoring at the same time. For grazing assessments this is likely to be during April to May. However, at this time of year it is more difficult to monitor invasion of heather areas by bracken or scrub. Ideally, monitoring should be during June to July when scrub and bracken will be most visible.

Step 2 An attempt should be made to cover the whole of the site to be monitored since one of the particular advantages of photographic monitoring is the possibility of recording unforeseen changes. On very large sites or groups of sites covering a large area, resources may not be available to cover all of the ground. In this case, a sample of the area must be selected. The most useful sample is likely to consist of areas in which there is heather identified as vulnerable to loss by grazing (diagnostics for which are described under Method 2) or susceptible to tree and shrub invasion. If this course is taken it must be accepted that it will be possible to state very little about what might be happening on non-vulnerable areas, and it will not be possible to record less predictable sources of damage such as accidental fires, drought damage, damage due to outbreaks of herbivorous insects or parasitic fungi, or influx of herbivores from adjacent land (e.g. deer from a forestry plantation).

Step 3 The use of markers such as fence stobs is required particularly on sites with relatively unbroken ground and little small-scale variation in topography or vegetation which could be used to aid relocation of photographic positions.

Step 6 It is suggested that both monochrome and colour photographs are used as each has particular advantages. Monochrome is more permanent, particularly if given archival processing. Colour slides can be projected to large sizes and can easily be superimposed by projection to check for any changes. Colour can be helpful for picking out the presence of scattered bracken, scrub, or dwarf shrubs other than heather, or heather damaged by heather beetle or winter dessication. Colour slides are also useful for talks or lectures or for illustrating publications.

Step 8 Very bright, sunny weather should be avoided when taking photographs as dense shadows, reflection and glare reduces the detail discernible in photographs. The automatic metering system of most good-quality modern cameras should produce correctly exposed photographs in most circumstances. Photographing into the light should be avoided where possible as without exposure correction the vegetation may be underexposed and, even if correctly exposed, vegetation detail is less perceptible.

<u>Time requirements</u>

A site of about 500 ha which is moderately hilly, offering a good range of vantage points covering all the site, will require about 15 to 20 fixed points. Selection of fixed points and putting in markers will take up to three to four man-days, depending on terrain and the availability of transport for materials. There will also be a requirement of one to two man-days per year to inspect and, as necessary, repaint identification numbers or replace missing markers. Taking the photographs will require one to two man-days, with about the same length of time required to inspect the photographs, draw heather boundaries on the base map and check for any changes.

Advantages and disadvantages

Photographic monitoring is a relatively rapid method but frequently requires more time than is realised. Time is required to set up a network of permanently marked fixed points and to check and renew these as necessary every year. Time is also required not just to take the photographs but also to analyse them so that changes in community boundaries or the distribution of a dominant species can be described in some sort of quantifiable way. Photographic monitoring is able to show only gross changes in cover of particular, distinctive dominant species (such as heather or bracken), and it can only reveal these some time after they have occurred. The inevitable lag in management response to loss of heather revealed by photographic monitoring means that, to reverse heather decline, more substantial changes in grazing or burning management may be needed than if the monitoring method had been able to predict potential heather loss and trigger a preventive management response. Photographic monitoring may allow prediction of further loss if accurate information about past and present stocking levels is available and stocking levels are stable. Frequently, this is not the case.

Apart from being relatively fast, photographic monitoring does have some other advantages, particularly when used as an adjunct to other techniques. The basic data set, made up of the photographs, requires no selectivity or subjective assessments in the field. This has two particular advantages. First, where monitoring is long-term and changes of field staff are likely, it reduces variability in results due to changes in recorders. Variability may still arise at the analysis stage but it is always possible to go back and check the original photographs and to cross check that staff are analysing the photographs consistently. Second, with complete detailed coverage, photographs can record changes whose importance was not foreseen at the start of the monitoring. It may not be possible to identify all vulnerable areas prior to monitoring, e.g. the precise areas where tree invasion may occur. They can also record features which are difficult to describe but which can be directly compared in photographs, e.g. patterns of patchiness of heather canopy. When used in conjunction with other techniques, photographic monitoring provides a backup record of change and a demonstration of these changes which can be much more convincing to non-scientists than statistical statements.

When to use this method

Photographic monitoring should be considered as part of all proposals for monitoring cover or assessing grazing intensity on heather. Where heather cover is being restored and stock levels have been reduced to well below those which may cause decline in heather cover (less than 0.5 ewes/ha or equivalent) then photographic monitoring will be an adequate minimum monitoring method. Where stock levels have been reduced but are still close to those which may be damaging, then one of the techniques for assessing grazing intensity and overgrazing effects on the heather should also be employed. Where increased grazing pressure and actual or potential loss of heather cover are suspected then, as a minimum, one should use the technique described next for rapid assessment of signs of overgrazing and heavy utilisation of vulnerable heather, in addition to photographic monitoring.

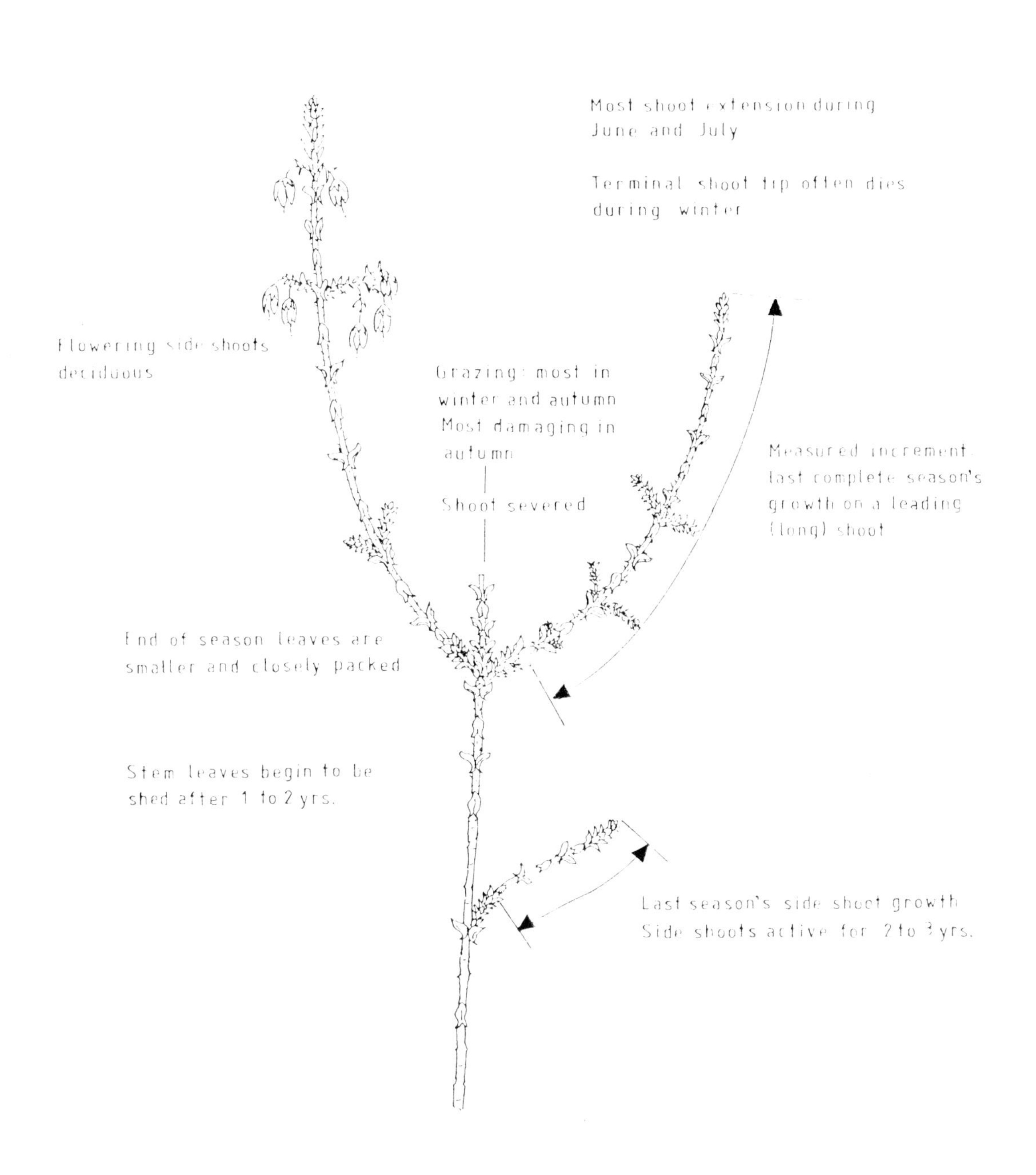

Figure 1 The structure of a heather shoot

Monitoring Method 2: rapid assessment of heather utilisation on selected areas with highest risk of overgrazing

Objectives

The aim of this method is to allow the rapid identification of heather which is most likely to be overgrazed, to assess if it is being overgrazed, and to enable a preliminary assessment of the probability of overgrazing of heather on the remainder of the site outside the identified vulnerable areas.

Procedure

1 This procedure is ideally carried out in April before there is significant new growth of heather shoots. The procedure can also be carried out relatively easily during March and May.

2 Vulnerable areas of heather should be identified using the following guidelines and marked on a map of the site (at 1:25,000 scale) or a recent aerial photograph of the same scale or larger (monochrome is adequate):

 (a) young heather, up to about five years old or about 15 cm tall, regenerating after a recent burn and particularly when it is mixed with a high proportion of grasses;

 (b) older heather which does not form a continuous canopy but is mixed with grass and herb species;

 (c) heather near to areas of more palatable bent/fescue Agrostis/Festuca grassland (within 50 m) particularly where this contains a high proportion of broadleaved grass species (more than 50%);

 (d) old heather stands in which the branches are beginning to collapse;

 (e) heather close to feeding stations.

3 Give each identified vulnerable area an individual identification code.

4 Through each vulnerable area walk transect lines with a spacing which results in at least five transects per mapped stand. At two regularly spaced points along each line stop and estimate the proportion of current heather long-shoot numbers which have been grazed in a notional 1 m x 1 m square (see Figure 1 for an illustration of heather long-shoots). Record these estimates then calculate the average for the whole of each vulnerable area.

5 If the average proportion of long-shoot numbers grazed is greater than 65% (i.e. two-thirds) then classify and record the area as presently overgrazed.

6 Also assess and record if the predominant growth form of the heather in each vulnerable area fits one of the following descriptions:

(a) a more-or-less prostrate carpet of dense, moderately contorted and intertwined branches (when occurring elsewhere than on exposed hill tops);

(b) relatively rounded, compact bushes in which there is a high degree of branching, with stems and branches frequently being contorted and intertwined ('topiary' heather);

(c) tight, rounded, small canopies of strongly contorted and intertwined branches on the end of a length of bare woody stem ('drumstick' or 'mop' heather).

Such areas should be recorded as having been chronically heavily grazed.

7 Estimate the proportion of vulnerable heather in each of the following categories from field records:

(a) presently overgrazed and also chronically heavily grazed;

(b) presently overgrazed only;

(c) chronically heavily grazed but not presently overgrazed.

8 Areas of vulnerable heather classified as being presently overgrazed should be photographed from a fixed point following the procedures described in Monitoring Method 1. Even if no substantial areas of vulnerable heather are identified as overgrazed, fixed point photographs should be taken of the heather boundary around feeding stations or where the heather is adjacent to bent/fescue grassland. Photographs should be taken from sufficiently close to the boundary to be able to discern a 2 m or larger change in the boundary.

9 If heather in the vulnerable areas is found to be overgrazed then the possibility of more widespread overgrazing should be checked by returning to the site in July-August and noting if:

(a) there is widespread grazing of heather at this time of year, particularly if this occurs on older, taller heather;

(b) other dwarf shrubs such as blaeberry/bilberry _Vaccinium myrtillus_ are heavily grazed and produce only short (less than 8 cm tall), little branched shoots rather than well-developed branched stems (when not suppressed by heather);

(c) grassland areas are very closely cropped to a sward height of less than 1.5 cm and there is an abundance of mosses, such as _Rhytidiadelphus squarrosus_, or bare ground within the sward;

(d) there are noticeable signs of grazing by sheep on unpalatable grasses such as mat-grass _Nardus stricta_ or purple moor-grass _Molinia caerulea_.

If all these indicators are present on the site then it is highly likely that substantial areas of heather not identified as vulnerable will also be overgrazed.

10 Keep a record of the results for comparison with repeat assessments.

11 Repeat the procedure in the following year if overgrazing or chronic past heavy grazing is identified. Continue till there have been five successive years of stable stock densities and management with no overgrazing of vulnerable heather areas for four of the five years. Thereafter repeat at five year intervals or when there is any change in stock densities, stock management or burning management. Fixed point photographs of vulnerable heather boundaries should be repeated at five year intervals even when no overgrazing is found and management is stable.

Comments on the procedure

Step 1 April is recommended as the best time to use this method because by then the previous season's shoot growth will have been grazed to its maximum extent, while new shoots, which tend not to be grazed much because new grass is available, have not grown sufficiently to obscure the shoots which have been grazed over winter. Estimates of proportions of shoots grazed can be made at other times of year but this becomes increasingly difficult in terms of assessment or interpretation the more remote this is from the optimum period.

Step 5 The grazing of 65% of heather long-shoots corresponds to a utilisation rate of about 40% of total long-shoot length. Paddock grazing studies by Grant et al. (1978, 1982) and Welch (1984 and pers. comm.) indicate that this level of utilisation will lead to a decline in percentage heather cover of about 4-5% per year within the area affected.

Step 6 The different growth forms of the heather result from heavy grazing at different stages of the heather growth cycle. Heavy grazing on young plants leads to the formation of the prostrate or carpet growth form. In this condition heather may persist through adventitious rooting of horizontal lateral branches, providing these do not become shaded out by unpalatable tussocky grasses such as mat-grass Nardus stricta or purple moor-grass Molinia caerulea. If heavy grazing does not occur till the heather is into mid-building stage or later then the 'topiary' or 'drumstick' growth form is produced. Heather in this state is unlikely to persist for long. The heather bushes are unlikely to produce new shoots from the base of the plant unless the canopy is quickly stripped by a short period of very intense grazing or by fire, but in very old bushes even this will not be successful. In old stands of heather, breakage of stems by stock trampling may be as damaging as the excessive offtake of new shoots and foliage.

Step 7 Complete loss of heather is likely to occur in categories (a) and (b) within 15 years or less (possibly considerably less, particularly in category (a)) if there is no change in stocking, stock management and/or burning management (see comments on Step 5).

Step 8 Loss of heather may occur in a very narrow band around feeding stations or patches of the strongly preferred bent/fescue grassland even if there is little sign elsewhere of overgrazing of heather. This can lead to a progressive erosion of heather cover. Once the losses become large they are likely to be picked up by the extensive photographic monitoring of Method 1 but it would be desirable to register such changes sooner since only then may remedial measures result in an improvement of stock management or burning practice.

Step 9 Although vulnerable heather may be overgrazed, this does not necessarily indicate that less vulnerable heather will also be overgrazed. This is particularly so if there is little shepherding, or if burning management results in a distribution of younger, more preferred, heather which encourages the sheep to concentrate within a limited part of the site.

Step 11 A misleading assessment of grazing intensity on heather may be obtained unless the assessment is repeated over a number of years. A good grass growing season may result in a significantly reduced amount of heather grazing over the following winter. There are considerable and unpredictable year-to-year variations in grass and heather production. Variation in heather productivity from one year to the next can be as high as ±50%, and for grassland ±70% (based on data in Frame, Newbould & Munro 1985; Jones & Tinsley 1980; Miller 1979; Moss & Miller 1976; Rawes & Welch 1969, and Smith & Forrest 1978). A five-year run of assessments is likely to be the minimum which will give a reasonable impression of the average grazing intensity under stable stocking and management conditions.

Time requirements

For a site of about 500 ha, two to three man-days should be sufficient.

Advantages and disadvantages

Careful observation and judgements which involve a subjective element are necessary and inevitable parts of this method. The precision of the estimates of heather utilisation will not be known. It can only provide circumstantial evidence that the heather on a site is being generally overgrazed. Also, a misleading assessment may be obtained if the method is not applied in more than one year due to considerable year-to-year variations in grass and heather production. Nevertheless, it is a simple and quick method to carry out since it does not require all heather on a site to be inspected carefully.

When to use this method

This method should be used when possible heather overgrazing is indicated by:

(a) cursory examination of the heather on the site;

(b) sheep stocking densities greater than 0.5 ewe/ha, or an equivalent stocking density if other herbivores are present.

It should also be used where there is anecdotal or documentary evidence of heather loss within the last decade.

Where overgrazing of non-vulnerable heather is indicated by this method, and where remedial changes in management are being considered, one of the following more systematic and objective methods of grazing intensity assessment and monitoring should be used.

Monitoring Method 3: rapid assesssment and mapping of heather utilisation over a whole site

Objectives

The aim of this method is to provide a rapid but comprehensive and systematic assessment of the extent of overgrazing over a whole site by applying to all the heather on a site the techniques for assessing heather utilisation described in Monitoring Method 2.

Procedure

1 Mapping is ideally carried out in April before there is significant growth of new heather shoots. It can also be undertaken relatively easily during March and May.

2 Mapping should be based on delineation of homogeneous stands of heather, site features which indicate potential vulnerability of heather, and areas of heavily modified or dead heather bushes. Mapping should be by direct field observation from vantage points (for which binoculars can be useful) aided by the use of aerial photographs. Monochrome photographs are perfectly adequate and should be at a scale of about 1:25000, although if they are available at a scale of 1:10000 this is even better. The more recent the photographs, the better. The Ordnance Survey in England, the Welsh Office and the Scottish Development Department hold details of recent aerial photograph coverage. Homogeneous stands will be definable on the aerial photographs by variations in tone, texture, and completeness of heather cover. Homogeneous stands and vulnerable areas should be mapped onto waterproof transparent overlays for the aerial photographs. An Ordnance Survey topographic map at the same scale, and any existing vegetation maps, may also be found helpful.

3 The following stand categories should be mapped where they occur in stands larger than 1 ha:

(a) recently burnt heather with a low vegetation cover;

(b) young regenerating heather stands. The sward/canopy height will be less than 15 cm and the vegetation will be recognisably short even from some distance. Heather cover will be variable and may be low. The cover of grasses such as wavy hair-grass Deschampsia flexuosa or other dwarf shrubs such as blaeberry/bilberry Vaccinium myrtillus may be high;

(c) areas of well developed, taller heather bushes intimately mixed with other species. The heather bushes will be erect and taller than about 30 cm;

(d) areas where there is a mosaic of small heather-dominated patches (each smaller than about 30 m x 30 m) among other vegetation;

(e) areas of complete heather dominance which are neither very short regenerating stands nor tall mature-to-old stands. The canopy height will be about 15 - 30 cm. These areas will appear dark and with a relatively even, fine texture on aerial photographs;

(f) areas of tall, mature or old heather, more than 30 cm tall, or with branch lengths longer than 30 cm, where holes may be developing in the canopy due to the outward collapse or death of central branches of large heather bushes;

(g) areas where the heather forms a short carpet or mat, less than 15 cm tall, of densely packed intertwined branches. Many of the branches will be growing horizontally or at an oblique angle and they may be more or less contorted. These areas may not be apparent till the ground is walked;

(h) areas where the heather bushes are taller than 15 cm, or do not form a carpet, and have compact, rounded canopies of densely packed, contorted and intertwined branches and shoots. The heather bushes may be in patches or may be individual bushes intimately mixed with other species. These areas may not be apparent till the ground is walked;

(i) areas of 'drumstick' or 'mop' heather in which heather bushes comprise lengths of bare woody stem each ending in a small rounded mass of contorted shoots and foliage;

(j) areas of dead heather canopy. If damage has been recent foliage and shoots will be orange-brown but this will gradually bleach to pale grey. Where only scattered bushes are involved the proportion of the heather stand affected should be estimated and noted. This may not be apparent till the ground is walked.

4 Each mapped area should be given an identifying code. In each mapped stand the proportion of the area occupied by a complete heather canopy should be estimated and noted.

5 Where the above stand types occur in patches of less than 1 ha but more than 400 m^2, e.g. forming a boundary zone around a favoured grazing area, they should be indicated on the map by a numbered target symbol and a note should be made of the estimated area of each patch.

6 Before further work is carried out all people involved in the mapping should spend a short time walking widely over the site to experience and practise assessing the full range of grazing intensity.

7 The next stage is to estimate grazing intensities in each mapped stand or target-noted patch. In each mapped stand parallel transect lines should be walked at a spacing that results in at least five transects in each mapped area. At two regularly spaced points along each transect line the proportion of heather long-shoot grazed should be estimated in notional 1 m x 1 m squares and noted. In each target note area five estimates should be made. The average of these estimates should then be calculated for each mapped stand or target note area.

8 The remainder of the method is the same as Steps 5, 6, 7, 8 and 10 of Monitoring Method 2 but is applied to all heather and not just vulnerable heather.

9 On at least one site, with stable management and within a local climatic region, repeat the procedure in the following year if overgrazing of heather not classified as vulnerable is identified.

Continue till there have been five successive years of stable stock densities and management with no overgrazing of non-vulnerable heather in four out of five of these years. Thereafter revert to using Monitoring Method 2. On other sites in the same local climatic region repeat after five years.

Comments on the procedure

Step 1 See comments on Step 1 of Method 2.

Step 3 The grazing intensity distribution over a site will be related to these stand types and their locations. Different herbivores prefer to graze vegetation of different heights: mountain hares prefer to graze heather less than 15 cm tall, sheep prefer heather less than 20 cm tall, red grouse prefer it 10 - 30 cm tall, and red deer prefer heather more than 25 cm tall (Moss *et al*. 1972; Savory 1974, 1986). Tall heather, more than 35 cm tall, restricts movement of animals smaller than deer and tends to be avoided by them.

Sheep prefer to graze heather which is:

- younger rather than older;
- shorter rather than taller;
- in sheltered locations rather than in more exposed locations;
- mixed with grasses, particularly when more palatable broadleaved grasses (such as bent species, sweet vernal-grass *Anthoxanthum odoratum* and heath-grass *Danthonia decumbens*) or sedges are present;
- near to areas of bent/fescue grassland, the more so as these include an increasing proportion of palatable broadleaved grass species and sedges;
- near to feeding stations.

Step 3(g) A dense carpet of heather can be produced by heavy grazing which begins when the heather plants are still young and have vigorous basal lateral branches which grow horizontally and are able to produce adventitious roots where they contact the ground. Any erect shoots are grazed but the apices of the horizontally-growing branches avoid damage. This growth form can also occur as a result of wind-clipping on exposed hill tops even where there is very little or no grazing pressure.

Step 3(h) and (i) These growth forms of heather result from heavy grazing, when this begins after well-developed bushes have formed.

Step 3(j) Areas of dead heather canopy may result from climatic damage such as winter dessication or prolonged burial by snow (with attack by snow mould), or damage by heather beetle. Trampling by animals and crushing by vehicles will also cause damage. Where damage has been sufficient to kill shoots they will become orange-brown immediately after damage. This is characteristic of all types of damage. After heather beetle damage, shoot tips and upper branches may be stripped of bark to varying degrees and may appear whitish. Damage may affect entire stands or it may affect only individual scattered bushes. Heavily grazed bushes may be more susceptible to damage (Watson *et al*. 1966) and grazing may promote the conversion of damaged areas to other vegetation types. Also, loss of heather due to these types of damage is additional to losses directly due to overgrazing.

Step 6 This helps to ensure consistency of estimation of grazing intensity.

Step 9 See comments for Step 11, Method 2. Only one site within a local climatic region need be monitored every year for five years. Other sites can be assessed in relation to the year-to-year variations in grazing intensities on heather shown on this site. A local climatic region should be taken to mean an area of about 2,000-3,000 km^2.

Time requirements

For a largely heather-dominated site of about 500 ha about five man-days will be required, if about half the heather has a small-scale burning management pattern like that on a grouse moor. There will be some variation in the time required, depending on precisely how much of the heather occurs as small stands.

Advantages and disadvantages

The advantages and disadvantages of this method are similar to those for Monitoring Method 2 of which this method is an extension. It provides a clearer indication of the occurrence of probable overgrazing for all the heather on a site but because of its more comprehensive coverage it does take longer to carry out.

When to use this method

This method should be used when Monitoring Method 2 has indicated that overgrazing may be occurring on heather which has not been classified as vulnerable. If confirmed by this method and remedial changes in management are proposed then Monitoring Method 4, which will provide utilisation data of determinable precision, should be used.

Monitoring Method 4: estimation of heather utilisation with a precision of ± 10% in strata of low, medium and high grazing intensity

Objectives

This method aims to provide an objective estimate of mean utilisation of total heather long-shoot length, with a 95% confidence interval around the mean of ± 10%, for each of three strata defined as low, medium and high grazing intensity and delineated using the data collected by Monitoring Method 3.

Procedure

1 This method should be carried out between April and June.

2 Carry out the procedure described in Monitoring Method 3.

3 Classify all the mapped heather stands according to the following class definitions:

(a) low grazing intensity: the mean proportion of shoot numbers grazed is less than or equal to 33%;

(b) medium grazing intensity: the mean proportion of shoot numbers grazed is greater than 33% but less than or equal to 65%;

(c) high grazing intensity: the mean proportion of shoot numbers grazed is greater than 65%.

4 Delineate the areas on the site which fall within each of the grazing intensity classes. These three types of area will form three strata for further plot-based sampling.

5 Within each grazing intensity stratum a number of plot locations are randomly selected and marked on the map and on aerial photographs of the site (so that they can be found on the ground). They should be in areas where the heather cover will be at least 33%. The number of plots required will depend on the time required to find and travel between plot locations. This should be estimated by:

(a) assuming an even scatter of seven locations in each of the low and medium strata, and 33 locations in the high stratum,

(b) calculating the average distance between locations in each stratum by dividing the area of each stratum by the number of locations and then taking the square root of the result, and

(c) calculating the average time to travel this distance, at a rate of 4.8 km/hr plus half an hour for every 300 m of uphill climb, and then adding 10 minutes for precisely locating and laying out each plot.

The numbers of plots required for various lengths of time taken to find and lay out each plot are shown below.

Time to find and lay out each plot (mins)	Number of plots per stratum in each stratum type		
	Low	Medium	High
15	9	7	33
30	6	6	33
60	6	6	24

6 Cut four lengths of a relatively non-stretchable type of string, such as builders' string, so that each will be 20 m long when stretched tight.

7 Take two of these strings and mark an identical pattern of 20 randomly located points on each string. The random points should be marked with crimped metal or wire tags or some other form of conspicuous and secure marker. These will be plot baseline strings.

8 Make three more pairs of baseline strings.

9 Cut a further 20 strings which also should be 20 m long when stretched tight. On each string mark five randomly located points. These are cross-strings used to locate randomly selected heather shoots.

10 Find a plot location on the ground with the help of the map of heather stands and the aerial photographs of the site. The precise position of the plot should be selected so that a 20 m x 20 m plot will have a heather cover of at least 33%.

11 Lay out a 20 m x 20 m square plot at the selected site using marker pegs and two unmarked strings plus a pair of baseline strings. The baseline strings should be on opposite sides of the plot with the pattern of random points marked on each orientated in the same direction.

12 Select at random a pair of corresponding points on the baseline strings and stretch a randomly selected cross-string between these two points.

13 At the random point marked on the cross-string lower a thin, sharpened pin vertically so that it glances the mark on the string. This can be carried out most easily if the pin is attached to the lower end of the centre column of a lightweight camera tripod. The tripod should have an integral or attached bubble level so that it can be levelled and the centre column made vertical. The legs should be quickly adjustable.

(a) From the point at which the pin point first touches a heather shoot, trace back down the shoot two years' increments. If there is a branch point at or just below this position then choose the thickest, most robust shoot and follow it back towards its apex. This should lead to a long shoot for which the most recent complete year's increment should be measured to the nearest millimetre in the high stratum, or noted as either grazed or ungrazed in the low and medium strata.

(b) If the shoot has been grazed (in the high stratum) then the length of increment remaining should be measured. If the pin first touches a thick branch then simply follow this up, selecting the thickest shoot at each branch point.

(c) If the pin first touches dead material then trace back to a live shoot, if necessary going back further than two increments.

(d) If the whole branch system is dead more-or-less to ground level, or the pin does not touch heather at all, then choose the nearest live shoot within 5 cm of the pin and then follow the above procedure to find the appropriate long shoot.

(e) If no shoots are found by these procedures then the random point on another cross-string at another baseline position should be inspected.

14 In the high stratum, if the selected long-shoot is grazed then select a nearby, similar, ungrazed long-shoot to estimate its pre-grazed length. The selected shoot should be in a similar position in the canopy, of the same thickness and woodiness, and with similar side-shoot and flowering zone structures, where these are present. Measure the most recent complete year's increment of this shoot to the nearest millimetre.

15 Repeat steps 12 to 14 until the required number of heather shoots have been selected and measured. If all 20 cross-strings have been used before sufficient shoots are selected then the baseline strings should be replaced by another pair and the process continued.

16 The number of shoots required per plot depends on the stratum type, the number of plots per stratum (see Step 5), and the time taken to travel to and lay out each plot, as shown below.

Time to find and lay out each plot (mins)	Number of shoots per plot in each stratum type		
	Low	Medium	High
15	20	30	5
30	50	30	5
60	50	50	10

17 (a) In the high grazing intensity stratum the proportion of heather long-shoot increment which has been grazed should be calculated for each plot using this formula:

$$\text{utilisation } (\%) = \frac{X - Y}{X + Z} \times 100$$

where X = total estimated pre-grazed shoot increment length in the shoot sample,

Y = total length of shoot increment remaining on grazed shoots in the sample,

Z = total ungrazed shoot increment length in the sample.

(b) In the medium and low grazing intensity strata the estimated utilisation should be calculated for each plot using the formula utilisation (%) = 0.61 x proportion of long-shoots grazed.

18 The mean of the plot utilisations in each stratum should be calculated. In most instances the 95% confidence limits around these means should be ± 10%.

19 If mean utilisation in the high grazing intensity stratum, or any other stratum, is greater than 40% then extensive heather loss is likely to occur within this stratum if stocking and management remain unchanged. Calculate the proportion of the heather on the site affected.

20 The procedure should be carried out once when Monitoring Method 3 indicates that overgrazing is occurring on non-vulnerable heather. If changes in herbivore densities or stock management are then brought about the procedure should be repeated in the April to June period following the change. Thereafter continue using Monitoring Method 3.

Comments on the procedure

Step 3 As discussed in the comments on Monitoring Method 2, 65% of shoot numbers grazed corresponds to a utilisation of about 40%, which best present evidence suggests is likely to lead to heather loss.

Steps 5 and 16 The combinations of number of plots per stratum and the number of shoots sampled per plot are the most time-efficient combinations which will give 95% confidence limits of ± 10%, assuming:

(a) an even gradation of utilisation from 0% - <18.5% in the low stratum, 18.5% - <40% in the medium stratum, and 40% - 100% in the high stratum;

(b) variances for the estimation of utilisation for each plot equal to the greatest plot variance found by the NCC Hill Vegetation Management Project on a test site in the Scottish Borders (plot variances were estimated using a 'bootstrap' procedure - see Step 17 & 18);

(c) 3.6 minutes to find and measure each sample shoot, or 30 seconds to find and assess if each shoot is grazed, based on sampling of 1,800 shoots in 18 plots carried out by the NCC Hill Vegetation Management Project on a test site in the Scottish Borders.

Step 10 If heather cover is less than 33% the selection of shoots becomes very time consuming as most random sample points then do not select a shoot.

Step 14 The Hill Vegetation Management Project found that, on its test site in the Scottish Borders, sheep (blackfaced ewes) selected for longer shoots in some plots. This means that an estimate of pre-grazed shoot length based on the lengths of the randomly selected ungrazed shoots will be an underestimate in some instances. Where selection for longer shoots occurred utilisation was underestimated by up to about half. This problem can largely be overcome if each grazed shoot is paired with a similar, nearby ungrazed shoot. In tests (two observers x two areas x 50 shoots) the Hill Vegetation Management Project obtained good correlations between real lengths and estimated lengths in an area of high heather cover (r^2 = 0.69 - 0.73) but less good in a relatively low heather cover area (r^2 = 0.30 - 0.38). There was some tendency to underestimate the length of very long shoots and overestimate the length of short shoots. Nevertheless, the estimates of mean shoot length were not significantly different from the real values (Mann Whitney U tests $p = 0.26$ to $p = 0.89$), and the calculated utilisations for sample plots were affected very little by these biases in shoot length estimation.

Step 17 and 18 The utilisation, as defined, is a ratio measure composed of a number of different variables. Statisticians have not yet devised simple procedures for calculating confidence limits for this type of measure using the variances of the component variables. However, the precision of the utilisation rate calculated for each plot can be estimated by applying a 'bootstrap' procedure to the data set for each plot. This involves using a computer to take a large number of repeated random samples (200 or more), with replacement, of shoot measurements from the data set for each plot with sample size equal to the number of shoots sampled in the plot. A utilisation is calculated for each sample. This generates a distribution of potential utilisation for each plot. From this it is possible to estimate the probability of obtaining a utilisation different from the one calculated using the set of shoot measurements actually sampled from the plot.

Step 18 The variance of the mean utilisation for each stratum has a component due to the sample variance within plots and a component due to the sample variance between plots. In most instances the sample variance within plots dominates - except in the high stratum.

Time requirements

Time requirements will vary according to the length of time it takes to find, travel between, and set out each plot, as shown below.

The man-days estimate is based on spending 6½ hours per day travelling between, laying out, and sampling plots. To these time estimates should be added the time to carry out Monitoring Method 3 which provides the data used to define the sample stratification. In total the combination of Monitoring Methods 3 and 4 will require 9-11 man-days for a site of about 500 ha.

Time required to find and lay out each plot (mins)	Time required per stratum for each stratum type (man-hours)			Total (man-hours)	Total (man-days)
	Low	Medium	High		
15	3.75	3.50	18.15	25.40	3.9
30	5.50	5.25	26.40	37.15	5.7
60	8.50	8.50	38.40	55.40	8.5

Advantages and disadvantages

This method provides estimates of utilisation of heather which can be statistically analysed. It allows an objective check to be made that areas mapped by Monitoring Method 3 as heavily grazed are actually being grazed at a damaging intensity, or that areas not mapped as heavily grazed are indeed below the threshold at which heather loss is likely. This applies only to each whole stratum. Even if the mean utilisation for the stratum is less than 40%, localised areas of overgrazing and heather loss could still occur within the stratum (probably as a result of lack of shepherding or poor burning management). However, the smaller the areas experiencing overgrazing the greater the effort needed for stratification and plot sampling, if they are to be separately assessed, while the potential heather loss is of diminishing consequence for the site as a whole. This method provides a reasonable compromise between a single objective estimate of utilisation for a whole site (which would be quick, cheap but insensitive), and an expensive and detailed method aimed at identifying every instance of localised overgrazing by sampling every heather stand.

When to use this method

Ideally, this method should be used when Monitoring Method 3 indicates that overgrazing may be occurring on at least some of the heather which is not classified as vulnerable, and when remedial changes in management are proposed. It should be carried out before and after a change in stock management to provide accurate and objective estimates of the changes in heather utilisation. These can then be used to aid the interpretation of the results of longer term monitoring using only Monitoring Methods 2 and 3. This method may also be required to 'fine-tune' stock densities on sites subject to unwanted scrub invasion so that grazing intensities are high enough to control tree and shrub regeneration but not so high as to lead to heather loss.

Acknowledgements

The detailed comments of Dr Chris Sydes (CSD Uplands, Nature Conservancy Council), Mr James Marsden (NCC Assistant Regional Officer, North-west England), Mr David Elias (Senior Warden, Berwyn National Nature Reserve) and Miss Sheila Grant (Macaulay Land Use Research Institute) are gratefully acknowledged.

Appendix Equivalent numbers of different herbivores

	In terms of intake	In terms of damage to heather (where known)
Hill ewe of about 45 kg	1	
Beef cow of about 500 kg	8-9	12
Pony/horse of about 500 kg	10	
Red deer hind (dry) of about 80 kg	2	

These conversion figures are based on the following references: Forbes *et al*. 1980; Kay & Staines 1981; and Welch 1984.

References

ANDERSON, P., & YALDEN, D.W. 1981. Increased sheep numbers and the loss of heather moorland in the Peak District, England. Biological Conservation, 20, 195-213.

BIBBY, C.J. 1988. Impacts of agriculture on upland birds. In: Ecological change in the Uplands, ed. by M.B. Usher & D.B.E. Thompson, 223-236. Blackwell Scientific Publications (British Ecological Society Special Publication No. 7).

FORBES, T.J., DIBB, C., GREEN, J.O., HOPKINS, A., & PEAL, S. 1980. Factors affecting the productivity of permanent grassland. Harley, Grassland Research Institute.

FRAME, J., NEWBOULD, P., & MUNRO, J.M.M. 1985. Herbage production from the hills and uplands. In: Hill and livestock production: symposium proceedings, ed. by T.J. Maxwell & R.G. Gunn, 9-37. Penicuik, British Society of Animal Production (Occasional Paper No. 10).

GRANT, S.A., BARTHRAM, G.T., LAMB, W.I.C., & MILNE, J.A. 1978. Effects of season and level of grazing on the utilisation of heather by sheep. 1. Responses of the sward. British Grassland Society. Journal, 33, 289-300.

GRANT, S.A., MILNE, J.A., BARTHRAM, G.J., & SOUTER, W.G. 1982. Effects of season and level of grazing on the utilisation of heather by sheep. 3. Longer term responses and sward recovery. Grass and Forage Science, 37, 311-326.

HOBBS, A.M. 1988. Conservation of leafy liverwort-rich Calluna vulgaris heath in Scotland. In: Ecological change in the Uplands, ed. by M.B. Usher & D.B.A. Thompson, 339-344. Edinburgh, Blackwell Scientific Publications (British Ecological Society Special Publication No. 7).

JONES, R.J.A., & TINSLEY, J. 1980. Hill land studies in the Grampian region of Scotland. 1. Effects of soil parent material, altitude and aspect on the herbage yields, composition and response of fertilizer treatments in the upper Don basin. Journal of Soil Science, 31, 363-370.

KAY, R.N.B., & STAINES, B.W. 1981. The nutrition of the red deer Cervus elaphus. Nutrition Abstracts and Reviews. Series B, 51, 601-622.

MILLER, G.R. 1979. Quantity and quality of the annual production of shoots and flowers by Calluna vulgaris in north-east Scotland. Journal of Ecology, 67, 109-129.

MOSS, R., & MILLER, G.R. 1976. Production, grazing and die-back of heather Calluna vulgaris in relation to numbers of red grouse Lagopus L. scoticus and mountain hare Lepus timidus in north-east Scotland. Journal of Applied Ecolology, 13, 369-377.

MOSS, R., MILLER, G.R., & ALLEN, S.E. 1972. The selection of heather by captive red grouse in relation to the age of the plant. Journal of Applied Ecology, 9, 771-782.

NATURE CONSERVANCY COUNCIL. 1987. Changes in the Cumbrian countryside, Peterborough, Nature Conservancy Council. (Research & survey in nature conservation No. 6.)

NATURE CONSERVANCY COUNCIL AND COUNTRYSIDE COMMISSION FOR SCOTLAND. 1988. National Countryside Monitoring Scheme, Scotland: Grampian. Battleby, Perth, Countryside Commission for Scotland and Nature Conservancy Council.

RATCLIFFE, D.A., & THOMPSON, D.B.A. 1988. The British uplands: their ecological character and international significance. In: Ecological change in the uplands, ed. by M.B. Usher & D.B.A. Thompson, 9-36, Edinburgh, Blackwell Scientific Publications (British Ecological Society Special Publication No. 7).

RAWES, M., & WELCH, D. 1969. Upland productivity of vegetation and sheep at Moor House National Nature Reserve, Westmorland, England. Oikos 11, Supplement, 7-72.

SAVORY, C.J. 1974. The feeding ecology of red grouse in north-east Scotland. Ph.D. Thesis, University of Aberdeen.

SAVORY, C.J. 1986. Utilisation of different ages of heather on three Scottish moors by red grouse, mountain hares, sheep and red deer. Holarctic Ecology, 9, 65-71.

SMITH, R.A.H., & FORREST, G.I. 1978. Field estimates of primary production. In: Production ecology of British moors and montane grasslands, ed. by O.W. Heal & D.F. Perkins, Ch. 2. Berlin, Springer-Verlag (Ecological Studies 27).

SYDES, C. 1988. Recent assessments of moorland losses in Scotland. Peterborough, Nature Conservancy Council. (CSD Note No. 43.)

THOMPSON, D.B.A., STROUD, D.A., & PIENKOWSKI, M.W. 1988. Afforestation and upland birds: consequences for population ecology. In: Ecological change in the Uplands, ed. by M.B. Usher & D.B.A. Thompson, 237-260. Edinburgh, Blackwell Scientific Publications (British Ecological Society Special Publication No. 7).

WATSON, A., MILLER, G.R., & GREEN, F.W.H. 1966. Winter browning of heather Calluna vulgaris and other moorland plants. Botanical Society of Edinburgh. Transactions, 10, 195-203.

WELCH, D. 1984. Studies in the grazing of heather moorland in north-east Scotland. II. Response of heather. Journal of Applied Ecology, 21, 197-207.

"Research & survey in nature conservation" series

No. 1 The use of permanent quadrats to record changes in the structure and composition of Wytham Woods, Oxfordshire. A S Horsfall and K J Kirby. 1985.

No. 2 Monitoring the abundance of butterflies 1976-1985. E Pollard, M L Hall and T J Bibby. 1986.

No. 3 Saltmarsh survey of Great Britain: Bibliography. Compiled by Kevin Charman, Wanda Fojt and Shirley Penny. 1986.

No. 4 A survey of the numbers and breeding distribution of the North Atlantic gannet Sula bassana and an assessment of the changes which have occurred since Operation Seafarer 1969/70. Sarah Wanless. 1987.

No. 5 Agricultural structures policy and nature conservation in Upland Grampian: a pilot study. J R Crabtree, Sue Evans, Brian J Revell and Philip M K Leat. 1987.

No. 6 Changes in the Cumbrian countryside. First report of the National Countryside Monitoring Scheme. 1987.

No. 7 The Wash and its environment. Report of a conference held on 8-10 April 1987 at Horncastle, Lincolnshire. Edited by Pat Doody and Brian Barnett. 1987.

No. 8 The moths of Ceredigion. A P Fowles. 1988.

No. 9 Long-term monitoring in unmanaged woodland nature reserves. G F Peterken and Christa Backmeroff. 1988.

No. 10 The woods of Argyll and Bute. Jane MacKintosh. 1988.

No. 11 A woodland survey handbook. K J Kirby. 1988.

No. 12 The reintroduction of the white-tailed sea eagle to Scotland: 1975-1987. Prepared by John A Love. 1988.

No. 13 Saltmarsh vegetation of the Wash. An assessment of change from 1971 to 1985. Margaret I Hill. 1988.

No. 14 The peatland management handbook. T A Rowell. 1988.

No. 15 Woodland conservation and research in the clay vale of Oxfordshire and Buckinghamshire. Proceedings of a symposium . . . on 14 March 1987. Edited by K J Kirby and F J Wright. 1988.

No. 16 NCC research in the uplands. Proceedings of a seminar, 1986. Edited by D B A Thompson, S Whyte and P H Oswald. 1988.

No. 17 The saltmarsh survey of Great Britain. An inventory of British saltmarshes. Fiona Burd. 1989.

No. 18 A sea-cliff bibliography. Compiled by Jonathan Mitchley. 1989.

No. 19 A botanical classification of standing waters in Great Britain and a method for the use of macrophyte flora in assessing changes in water quality. Margaret Palmer. 1989.

No. 20 Vegetated shingle structures survey of Great Britain: Bibliography. Pippa Sneddon and R E Randall. 1989.

No. 21 Dungeness bibliography. Compiled by Helen Riley (assisted by Brian Ferry). 1989.

No. 22 Inventories of ancient, long-established and semi-natural woodland for Scotland. G J Walker and K J Kirby. 1989.

No. 23 The Nature Conservancy Council's research programme (1989/90 edition). Compiled and edited by Philip Oswald and Stefa Birkenhead. 1989.

No. 24 Cut-over lowland raised mires. Proceedings of a conference held on 4 and 5 October 1988 at Doncaster. Edited by Wanda Fojt and Roger Meade. 1989.

No. 25 Moorland management: a literature review. M A Mowforth and C Sydes. 1989.

No. 26 Dungeness: a vegetation survey of a shingle beach. Bryan Ferry, Ned Lodge and Stephen Waters. 1989.

No. 27 Methods for monitoring heather cover. Angus MacDonald and Helen Armstrong. 1989.